Charlie's News Quips

G000042761

Charlie Haylock and Barrie Appleby

COUNTRYSIDE BOOKS

NEWBURY BERKSHIRE

First published 2014
Text and illustrations © Charlie Haylock and Barrie Appleby 2014

COUNTRYSIDE BOOKS
3 Catherine Road
Newbury
Berkshire
RG14 7NA

To view our complete range of books, please visit us at
www.countrysidebooks.co.uk

ISBN 978 1 84674 3306

Cover designed by Jason Appleby, The Ark Design Consultancy Ltd., Sudbury, Suffolk

Produced by The Letterworks Ltd., Reading
Typeset by KT Designs, St Helens
Printed by Berforts Information Press, Oxford

Foreword

The phone rang in the spring of 2013. 'I've got an idea, dear boy,' said Charlie Haylock.

I've known Charlie for a decade – have written about his books on the Suffolk dialect and the way we used to live – and his ideas are invariably good. (The bookshop chains might choose a different description, having endured his polite but persistent urgings to ignore head office diktat and do a better job of promoting local titles. He knows what he's talking about: his *Sloightly On Th'Huh* outsold *The Da Vinci Code* at the biggest bookshop in Ipswich.)

Howsumever (as Charlie is wont to say) we met at the Saracen's Head. The idea was indeed good: a weekly cartoon in the *East Anglian Daily Times*, taking a wry look at the news. It would ensure the weekend started with a smile.

While the words would be Charlie's, the artwork would showcase the genius of Barrie Appleby.

Who would have thought that the artist who draws Dennis the Menace and Roger the Dodger for the *Beano* comic would live in Suffolk? I was a bit starstruck – and envious. For Barrie's got the knack of showing with the subtle curve of a line exactly what a character is thinking.

It wasn't long before the first cartoon appeared and the series found a place in the hearts of readers sharing Charlie and Barrie's outlook on life.

You see, a true Suffolk person knows what is to be valued and what is frippery. He has a keen nose for cant, hypocrisy, arrant nonsense and over-blown ego. Pushed too far, he'll have his say – but the deft put-down will be gentle and accompanied by a twinkle in the eye.

The lad who blew the whistle on the emperor's new clothes would have come from Polstead or Pettistree, Risby or Rushmere St Andrew.

I've had the pleasure of being the first to view each week's offering. They used to arrive as a drawing on a piece of paper. Then, get this, they started coming by email as jpg files. *Thas a rum owd dew*, I mused.

Charlie and Barrie, it has been a privilege to laugh with you. That idea you had, *thas suffen good*.

Steven Russell
East Anglian Daily Times

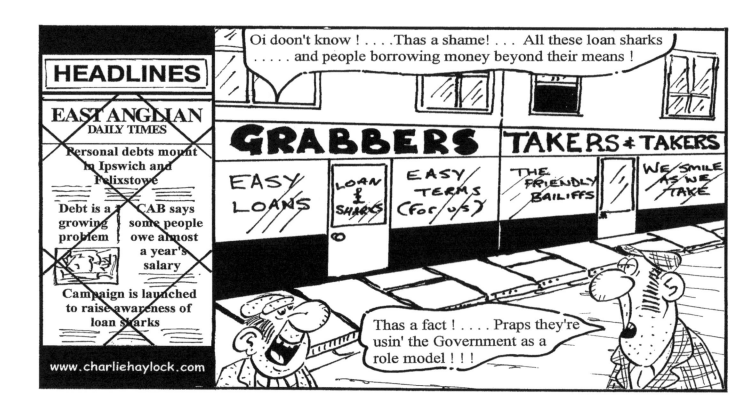

Charlie's News Quips

Withdrawn Cartoons

I've been brought up with the *East Anglian Daily Times*. ... I remember my grandparents reading and listening to the EADT ... yes ... listening! They would take it in turns at the end of the day to read news articles to each other ... and then have a full discussion on the various news stories ... . I had my own version of 'Newsnight' and 'Panorama' all rolled into one. And these wise owd country folk made more sense than the TV presenters.

We are very lucky in Suffolk to have a free-speaking daily newspaper, that deals with local, national and international news ... concentrating on the local. Reporting in an honest and straightforward way without a political bias is a narrow difficult path to follow ... and the 'East Anglian' achieves this ... but will not shy away from important issues and campaigns. Recently, both sides of the argument re Bentwaters airfield were equally explained for readers to decide ... and the EADT also led the way in the 'No Pylons' and the 'Get Connected' campaigns.

Very occasionally, a couple or three of our cartoons have quite rightly been withdrawn at the last minute, just before going to press. One such cartoon was commenting on the 11% pay rise for MPs, and made a general observation that was quite pertinent. ... But then a breaking news story changed the situation ... Tim Yeo, the South Suffolk MP, was deselected by his constituency, and he was going to appeal against the decision. The cartoon was now, very pointed towards Mr Yeo. Obviously, the EADT acted responsibly and withdrew the cartoon, else the supporters of Mr Yeo could accuse them of being politically biased against their local MP. Now the situation has been resolved, and we have included that cartoon here.

Another one 'pulled' depicted the horse doping scandal at Newmarket ... the breaking news which changed the situation was that only one trainer was accused and charged. ... The cartoon quite rightly had to be withdrawn as it would have looked as if we were making a biased comment on the trainer before the hearing. Now with the hearing over and judgment passed ... we can show the cartoon.

Charlie Haylock

Charlie's News Quips

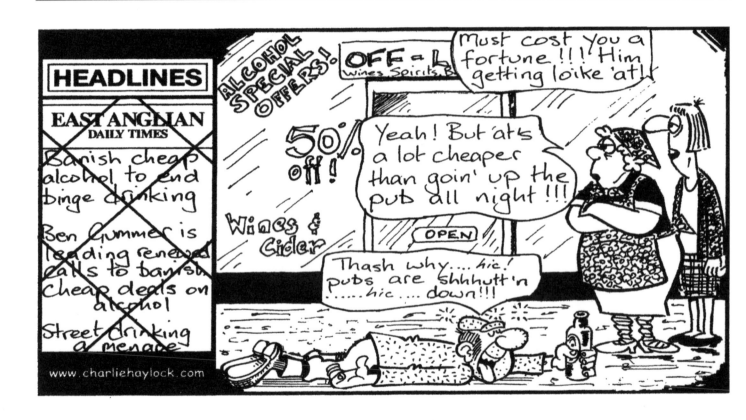

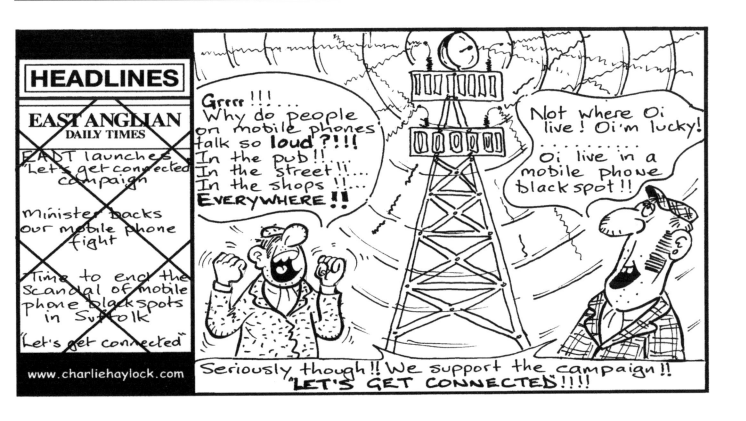

Charlie's News Quips

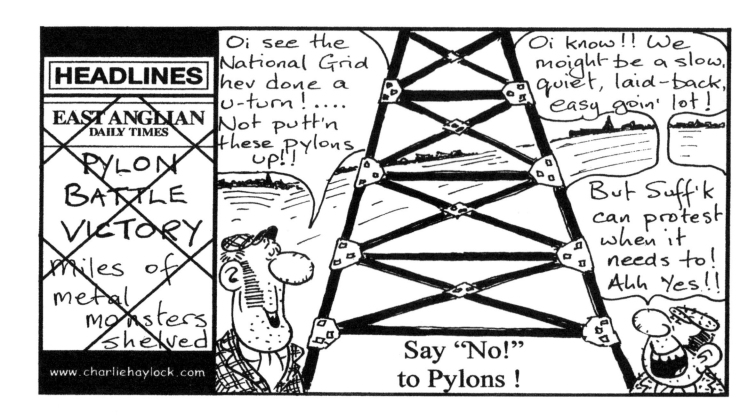

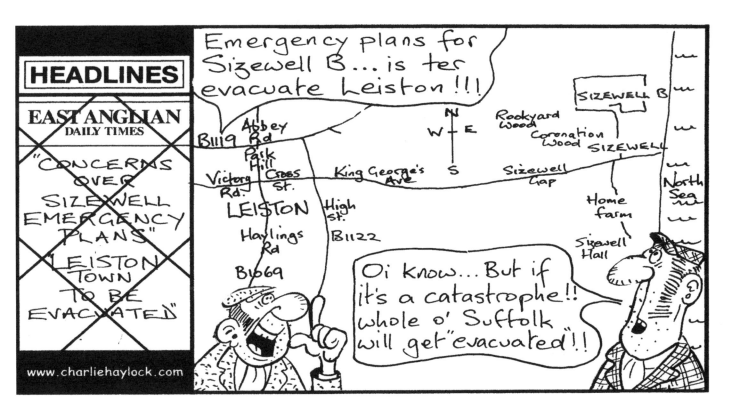

Charlie's News Quips

The Gardener's Revenge

Owd Billy Bloomfield was a self-employed gardener ... a hard working man and a God fearing one at that ... and very well respected in the village. He went to church regularly on Sundays ... sang a beautiful low deep bass in the St Mary the Virgin's Church choir ... was also Captain of the Tower for the local bellringing team ... and a long standing churchwarden. ... A pillar of country life.

This story starts on a hectic spring day, when Owd Billy had more than his fair share of work ... many wanting jobs doing that should have been done in the autumn, (retired city dwellers ... you know the sort) ... some wanting an instant garden and not realising that seeds and plants have to germinate and grow ... all in a hurry ... (and that don't do!)

Well, Owd Billy finished his morning job at the vicarage for the Rev. Basil Pargetter-Smythe ... funny owd boy the vicar ... very upright and the 'hell fire and brimstone' sort ... very strict and not much leniency and forgiveness ... . No! ... not very religious really in the true sense of the word I suppose ... very stern ... but the vicar did have one obsession. ... He was a keen radio ham ... (trying to get nearer his maker, I reckon) ... and one Sunday said, 'Over and out!' instead of 'Amen' .... that caused a stir ... and a fair few of the kids in the village were christened, 'Roger' ... including two girls!

Howsumever, the Rev. Basil paid Owd Billy in cash, 'Thankyer koindly, vicar ... must dash ... I've got the vegetable gardens to attend to at the Rose and Crown ... got ter be there by twelve noon ... and I'm on the drag ... . See yer tomorrer at choir practice ... cheerio, vicar!' and Owd Billy touched the peak of his cap and then, with his owd distinctive blue wooden wheelbarrow and gardening tools, dashed off to the pub as fast as he could.

Owd Billy got to the Rose and Crown two minutes late ... the side door through to the vegetable gardens was therefore locked, and the landlord, owd Albert 'Short Measure' Armstrong, was just opening up for the lunch time session. 'Haven't got time to open the side gate now ... you're late. ... You'll have to go through the public bar and tap room to get to the garden!'

Owd Billy knew he couldn't get his owd distinctive blue wooden wheelbarrow through the tight corridors ... so he left it outside ... picked up his tools and went through the pub to the vegetable gardens at the back ... . There was hell 'n' all to do ... specially if they needed the vegetables for the pub meals ... .

Owd Billy worked his socks off ... hoeing, weeding, clearing away, planting etc etc. ... 'Short Measure' closed the pub at 2.30 pm ... (no all day opening in them days) ... and came out with a cuppa tea and a couple a three arrowroot biscuits for Owd Billy. 'There you are, Billy boy ... doubt whether you'll finish today ... see you tomorrow ... must go in for my afternoon nap.'

Owd Billy soon devoured that little lot and carried on working 'til 6.00 pm .. the same time as opening time at the Rose and Crown. ... He took all his gear through the pub ... 'Short Measure' remarked on how hard Owd Billy had worked and asked if he wanted a swift pint. 'No thank yer koindly,' say Owd Billy. 'Want ter get hoom fer me dinner ... see yer tomorrer ... same toime.'

Next day was much the same for Owd Billy. He had an urgent job ... this time at the owd Major's, just the other side of the war memorial on the village green. ... Major Jonathan 'Whatto' Gildersleeve was a typical 'up 'em and at 'em' major with a very loud Harrow School accent, ... ending every sentence with a booming 'Whatto!' ... all the time Owd Billy was cutting and pruning ... Major 'Whatto' was rattling on about how he had won the war, and poor Owd Billy was getting more and more on the drag ... . Eventually he finished all the jobs ... simply packed his tools into the owd distinctive blue wooden wheelbarrow and said, 'Must away ... see you at choir practice tonight.'

Well ... Owd Billy was on the drag again for his afternoon work at the Rose and Crown. ... He got there two minutes late again ... the side door was still locked, and owd 'Short Measure' was opening up. 'Haven't got time to open the side gate now ... you're late ... you'll have to go through the public bar and tap room to get to the garden!'

So Owd Billy left his distinctive blue wheelbarrow outside again ... picked up his tools and went through the pub to the back garden as before. ... There was still hell 'n' all to do ... Owd Billy slaved away all afternoon ... . 'Short Measure' closed the pub at 2.30 pm as usual ... and came out with a cuppa and a few more arrowroot biscuits ... disappeared for his afternoon nap ... and left Owd Billy to get on with it. ... He finished just after 6.00 pm ... picked up his tools, and

went through to the tap room to see 'Short Measure' Armstrong to get paid for his labours. ... Owd Billy got paid in cash, refused a free pint and dashed off out saying he had to rush home and get ready for choir practice.

As he picked up his distinctive blue wooden wheelbarrow outside the Rose and Crown, he was met by the village busybody and gossip, owd Miss 'Snouty' Snodgrass. A 50-year-old spinster who rose early in the morning ... and went to bed every night at 8.00 pm. ... And was even stricter than the vicar when it came to religion.

Well ... poor Owd Billy couldn't get a word in edgeways. ... Owd Miss 'Snouty' verbally laid into he, 'You should be ashamed of yourself ... staying in the pub all afternoon ... two days running ... and having a lock-in when the pub ought to be closed. ... I'll tell the vicar about you ... thought you were a God fearing man ... you are a disgrace to the Church ... . It says in the Bible that drink is evil ... and you are evil ... alcohol is the enemy ... . You won't be a churchwarden after this ... you wait and see ... . And you'll lose your place in the choir ... . And the end of your bellringing days ... . You ... '

Owd Billy just doffed his cap and went off home, leaving owd Miss 'Snouty' ranting and raving all on her own. He arrived home, had his evening meal and got ready for choir practice ... but tonight was different ... . He took his distinctive blue wooden wheelbarrow and left it in the aisle ... everyone wondered why ... . Owd Billy explained he had an urgent job later that evening and would have to leave ten minutes early.

Choir practice went well and it was time for Owd Billy to leave ... . He bid farewell ... picked up his wheelbarrow ... and left the church. ... As he got to owd Miss 'Snouty' Snodgrass's cottage, he quietly walked up to her garden gate ... parked up his distinctive blue wooden wheelbarrow ... and went home ... leaving it there ... all night! ... For all to see! ... Including the vicar!

Revenge indeed !

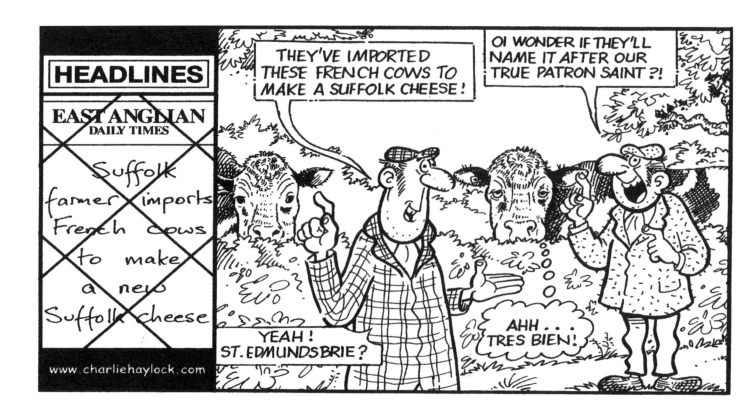

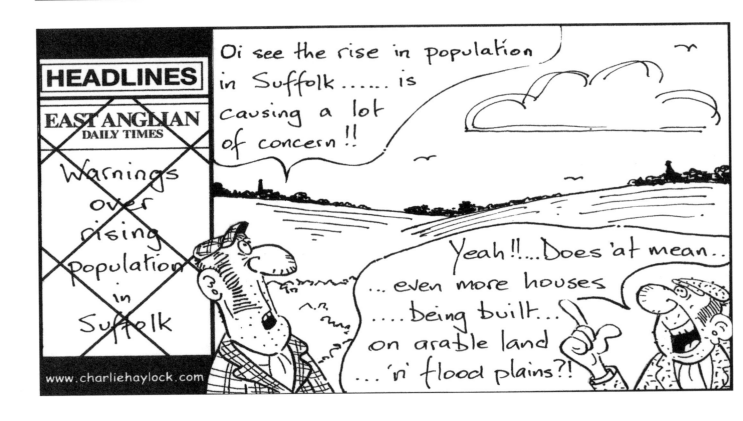

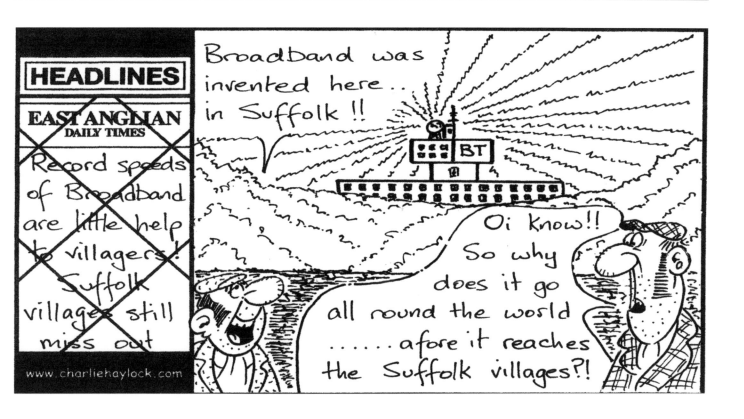

Charlie's News Quips

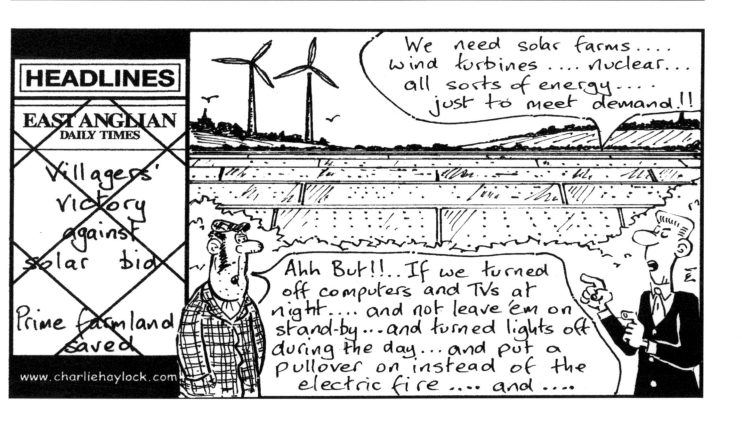

Charlie's News Quips